The Old Gumbie Cat

So she's formed from that lot of dis-or-der-ly louts,— a troop of well-dis-ci-plined,

So she's formed from that lot of dis-or-der-ly louts,— a troop of well-dis-ci-plined,

wan-ton des-troy-ment.

doo doo doo doo doo doo doo

wan-ton des-troy-ment.

doo doo doo doo doo doo doo

help-ful boy scouts, With a pur-pose in life — and a good deed to do; and she's ev-en cre-a-ted a Bee-tles' Tat-too.

help-ful boy scouts, With a pur-pose in life — and a good deed to do; and she's ev-en cre-a-ted a Bee-tles' Tat-too.

doo doo doo doo With a pur-pose in life — and a good deed to do; and she's ev-en cre-a-ted a Bee-tles' Tat-too.

doo doo doo doo With a pur-pose in life — and a good deed to do; and she's ev-en cre-a-ted a Bee-tles' Tat-too.

Bustopher Jones: the cat about town

Lyrics visible in the score:

he's the St. James-'s Street cat!
such an im-pec-ca-ble
He's the

bwa bwa bwa

back. ooh
back. ooh
back. In the whole of St. James-'s the smart-est of names is the name of this Brum-mell of

bwa bwa bwa bwa bwa bwa

And we're all of us proud to be nod-ded or bowed to by
And we're all of us proud to be nod-ded or bowed to by
cats; And we're all of us proud to be nod-ded or bowed to by

bwa bwa bwa bwa bwa bwa

* ⌇⌇⌇ = wide vibrato

Memory

22

Skimbleshanks: the railway cat

Choral Programme Series

For mixed voices:

French Chansons – Saint-Saëns/Fauré/Debussy
SATB & SATB/piano. Edited by Timothy Brown

Antonín Dvořák – Four choruses for mixed voices Op 29
SATB. Edited by Jan Smaczny

Gustav Holst – Five Partsongs Op 12
SATB

Felix Mendelssohn – Four Sacred Partsongs
SATB (div). Edited by Judith Blezzard

C.H.H. Parry – Seven Partsongs
SATB

Franz Schubert – Four Partsongs
SATB/keyboard. Edited by Judith Blezzard

C.V. Stanford – Seven Partsongs
SATB

Ralph Vaughan Williams – Three Choral Hymns
SATB/organ or piano

Gilbert & Sullivan – Opera Choruses 1
SATB/keyboard. Edited by Ronald Corp

Gilbert & Sullivan – Opera Choruses 2
SATB/keyboard. Edited by Ronald Corp

Five English Folksongs
SATB. Arranged by Daryl Runswick

Five American Folksongs
SATB. Arranged by Daryl Runswick

Memory and other choruses from 'Cats'
SATB/piano. Lloyd Webber, arranged by Peter Gritton

For upper voices:

Franz Schubert – Three Partsongs
SSAA/piano. Edited by Judith Blezzard

English Edwardian Partsongs
SSA/piano

Memory and other choruses from 'Cats'
SSA/piano. Lloyd Webber, arranged by Gwyn Arch

Mr Mistoffelees and other choruses from 'Cats'
SSA/piano. Lloyd Webber, arranged by Gwyn Arch

ISBN 0-571-51339

Faber Music 3 Queen Square London WC1N 3AU

9 780571 513390